20889

Science and
Human Values

Science and
Human Values

BY J. BRONOWSKI

HARPER TORCHBOOKS 🔥 THE SCIENCE LIBRARY

HARPER & ROW, PUBLISHERS

New York and Evanston

CONTENTS

1   The Creative Mind   7

2   The Habit of Truth   33

3   The Sense of Human Dignity   63

ILLUSTRATIONS

Part 1: Glad Day *by William Blake*

Part 2: Portrait of a Lady with An Ermine
by Leonardo Da Vinci

Part 3: Old Man Fettered *from The First Book of
Urizen by William Blake*

Page 20: Planetary Orbits Embedded in the Regular
Solids. *Illustration from Kepler's Mysterium
Cosmographicum, 1596*

Page 38: The Proportions of the Human Figure After
Vitruvius *by Leonardo Da Vinci*

FRONTISPIECE AND HALF-TITLE PAGE DECORATIONS: The
Ancient of Days Striking the First Circle of the Earth
by William Blake

1 The
Creative Mind

1.

ON a fine November day in 1945, late in the afternoon, I was landed on an airstrip in Southern Japan. From there a jeep was to take me over the mountains to join a ship which lay in Nagasaki Harbour. I knew nothing of the country or the distance before us. We drove off; dusk fell; the road rose and fell away, the pine woods came down to the road, straggled on and opened again. I did not know that we had left the open country until unexpectedly I heard the ship's loudspeakers broadcasting dance music. Then suddenly I was aware that we were already at the center of damage in Nagasaki. The shadows behind me were the skeletons of the Mitsubishi factory buildings, pushed backwards and sideways as if by a giant hand. What I had thought to be broken rocks was a concrete power house with its roof punched in. I could now make out the outline of two crumpled gasometers; there was a cold furnace festooned with service pipes; otherwise nothing but cockeyed telegraph poles and loops of wire in a bare waste of ashes. I had blundered into this desolate landscape as instantly as one might wake among the craters of the moon. The moment of recognition when I realized that I was already in Nagasaki is present to me as I write, as vividly as when I lived it. I see the warm night and the meaningless shapes; I can even remember the tune that was coming from the ship. It was a dance tune which had been popular in 1945, and it was called "Is You Is Or Is You Ain't Ma Baby?"

This book, which I have called *Science and Human Values*, was born at that moment. For the moment I have recalled was a universal moment; what I met was, almost as abruptly, the experience of mankind. On an evening like that evening, some time in 1945, each of us in his own way learned that his imagination had been dwarfed. We looked up and saw the power of which we had been proud loom over us like the ruins of Nagasaki.

The power of science for good and for evil has troubled other minds than ours. We are not here fumbling with a new dilemma; our subject and our fears are as old as the tool-making civilizations. Men have been killed with weapons before now: what happened at Nagasaki was only more massive (for 40,000 were killed there by a flash which lasted seconds) and more ironical (for the bomb exploded over the main Christian community in Japan). Nothing happened in 1945 except that we changed the scale of our indifference to man; and conscience, in revenge, for an instant became immediate to us. Before this immediacy fades in a sequence of televised atomic tests, let us acknowledge our subject for what it is: civilization face to face with its own implications. The implications are both the industrial slum which Nagasaki was before it was bombed, and the ashy desolation which the bomb made of the slum. And civilization asks of both ruins: "Is You Is Or Is You Ain't Ma Baby?"

2.

The man whom I imagine to be asking this question, wryly with a sense of shame, is not a scientist; he is civilized man. It is of course more usual for each member of civilization to take flight from its consequences by protesting that others have failed him. Those whose education and perhaps tastes have confined them to the humanities protest that the scientists alone are to blame, for plainly no mandarin ever made a bomb or an industry. The scientists say, with equal contempt, that the Greek scholars and the earnest explorers of cave paintings do well to wash their hands of blame; but what in fact are they doing to help direct the society whose ills grow more often from inaction than from error?

This absurd division reached its *reductio ad absurdum*, I think, when one of my teachers, G. H. Hardy, justified his great life work on the ground that it could do no one the least harm—or the least good. But

Hardy was a mathematician; will humanists really let him opt out of the conspiracy of scientists? Or are scientists to forgive Hardy because, protest as he might, most of them learned their indispensable mathematics from his books?

There is no comfort in such bickering. When Shelley pictured science as a modern Prometheus who would wake the world to a wonderful dream of Godwin, he was alas too simple. But it is as pointless to read what has happened since as a nightmare. Dream or nightmare, we have to live our experience as it is, and we have to live it awake. We live in a world which is penetrated through and through by science and which is both whole and real. We cannot turn it into a game simply by taking sides.

And this make-believe game might cost us what we value most: the human content of our lives. The scholar who disdains science may speak in fun, but his fun is not quite a laughing matter. To think of science as a set of special tricks, to see the scientist as the manipulator of outlandish skills—this is the root of the poison mandrake which flourishes rank in the comic strips. There is no more threatening and no more degrading doctrine than the fancy that somehow we may shelve the responsibility for making the decisions of our society by passing it to a few scientists armored with a special magic. This is another dream, the dream of H. G. Wells, in which the tall elegant engineers rule, with perfect benevolence, a humanity which has no business except to be happy. To H. G. Wells this was a dream of heaven—a modern version of the idle, harp-resounding heaven of other childhood pieties. But in fact it is the picture of a slave society and should make us shiver whenever we hear a man of sensibility dismiss science as someone else's concern. The world today is made, it is powered by science; and for any man to abdicate an interest in science is to walk with open eyes towards slavery.

My aim in this book is to show that the parts of civilization make a whole: to display the links which give society its coherence and, more, which give it life. In particular, I want to show the place of science in the canons of conduct which it has still to perfect.

This subject falls into three parts. The first is a study of the nature of the scientific activity, and with it of all those imaginative acts of understanding which exercise *The Creative Mind.* After this it is logical to ask what is the nature of the truth, as we seek it in science and in social life and to trace the influence which this search for empirical truth has had on conduct. This influence has prompted me to call the second part *The Habit of Truth.* Last I shall study the conditions for the success of science and find in them the values of man which science would have had to invent afresh if man had not otherwise known them: the values which make up *The Sense of Human Dignity.*

This, then, is a high-ranging subject which is not

to be held in the narrow limits of a laboratory. It disputes the prejudice of the humanist who takes his science sourly and, equally, the petty view which many scientists take of their own activity and that of others. When men misunderstand their own work, they cannot understand the work of others; so that it is natural that these scientists have been indifferent to the arts. They have been content, with the humanists, to think science mechanical and neutral; they could therefore justify themselves only by the claim that it is practical. By this lame criterion, they have of course found poetry and music and painting at least unreal and often meaningless. I challenge all these judgements.

3.

There is a likeness between the creative acts of the mind in art and in science. Yet, when a man uses the word science in such a sentence, it may be suspected that he does not mean what the headlines mean by science. Am I about to sidle away to those riddles in the Theory of Numbers which Hardy loved, or to the heady speculations of astrophysicists, in order to make claims for abstract science which have no bearing on its daily practice?

I have no such design. My purpose is to talk about science as it is, practical and theoretical. I define science as the organization of our knowledge in such a way that it commands more of the hidden potential in nature. What I have in mind therefore is both deep and matter of fact; it reaches from the kinetic theory of gases to the telephone and the suspension bridge and medicated toothpaste. It admits no sharp boundary between knowledge and use. There are of course people who like to draw a line between pure and applied science; and oddly, they are often the same people who find art unreal. To them, the word useful is a final arbiter, either for or against a work; and they use this word as if it can mean only what makes a man feel heavier after meals.

There is no sanction for confining the practice of science in this or another way. True, science is full of useful inventions. And its theories have often been made by men whose imagination was directed by the uses to which their age looked. Newton turned naturally to astronomy because it was the subject of his day; and it was so because finding one's way at sea had long been a practical preoccupation of the society into which he was born. It should be added, mischievously, that astronomy also had some standing because it was used very practically to cast horoscopes. (Kepler used it for this purpose; in the Thirty Years' War, he cast the horoscope of Wallenstein which wonderfully told his character, and he predicted a universal disaster for 1634 which proved to be the murder of Wallenstein.)

In a setting which is more familiar, Faraday worked all his life to link electricity with magnetism because this was the glittering problem of his day; and it was so because his society, like ours, was on the lookout for new sources of power. Consider a more modest example today: the new mathematical methods of automatic control, a subject sometimes called cybernetics, have been developed now because this is a time when communication and control have in effect become forms of power. These inventions have been directed by social needs, and they are useful inventions; yet it was not their usefulness which dominated and set light to the minds of those who made them. Neither Newton nor Faraday, nor yet Professor Norbert Wiener, spent their time in a scramble for patents.

What a scientist does is compounded of two interests: the interest of his time and his own interest. In this his behavior is no different from any other man's. The need of the age gives its shape to scientific progress as a whole. But it is not the need of the age which gives the individual scientist his sense of pleasure and of adventure and that excitement which keeps him working late into the night when all the useful typists have gone home at five o'clock. He is personally involved in his work, as the poet is in his and as the artist is in the painting. Paints and painting, too, must have been made for useful ends; and language was developed, from whatever beginnings, for practical communication. Yet you cannot have a man handle paints or language or the symbolic concepts of physics, you cannot even have him stain a miscroscope slide, without instantly waking in him a pleasure in the very language, a sense of exploring his own activity. This sense lies at the heart of creation.

The sense of personal exploration is as urgent, and as delightful, to the practical scientist as to the theoretical. Those who think otherwise are confusing what is practical with what is humdrum. Good humdrum work without originality is done every day by every one, theoretical scientists as well as practical, and writers and painters too, as well as truck drivers and bank clerks. Of course the unoriginal work keeps the world going; but it is not therefore the monopoly of practical men. And neither need the practical man be unoriginal. If he is to break out of what has been done before, he must bring to his own tools the same sense of pride and discovery which the poet brings to words. He cannot afford to be less radical in conceiving and less creative in designing a new turbine than a new world system.

And this is why in turn practical discoveries are not made only by practical man. As the world's interest has shifted, since the Industrial Revolution, to the tapping of new springs of power, the theoretical scientist has shifted his interests too. His speculations about energy have been as abstract as once they were about astronomy; and they have been profound now as they were then, because the man loved to think. The Carnot cycle and the dynamo grew equally from this love, and so did nuclear physics and the German V weapons and Kelvin's interest in low temperatures. Man does not invent by following either use or tradition; he does not invent even a new form of communication by calling a conference of communication engineers. Who invented the television set? In any deep sense, it was Clerk Maxwell who foresaw the existence of radio waves, and Heinrich Hertz who proved it, and J. J. Thomson who discovered the electron. This is not said in order to rob any practical man of the invention, but from a sad sense of justice; for neither Maxwell nor Hertz nor J. J. Thomson would take pride in television just now.

Man masters nature not by force but by understanding. This is why science has succeeded where magic failed: because it has looked for no spell to cast on nature. The alchemist and the magician in the Middle Ages thought, and the addict of comic strips is still encouraged to think, that nature must be mastered by a device which outrages her laws. But in four hundred years since the Scientific Revolution we have learned that we gain our ends only *with* the laws of nature; we control her only by understanding her laws. We cannot even bully nature by any insistence that our work shall be designed to give power over her. We must be content that power is the by-product of understanding. So the Greeks said that Orpheus played the lyre with such sympathy that wild beasts were tamed by the hand on the strings. They did not suggest that he got this gift by setting out to be a lion tamer.

What is the insight with which the scientist tries to see into nature? Can it indeed be called either imaginative or creative? To the literary man the question may seem merely silly. He has been taught that science is a large collection of facts; and if this is true, then the only seeing which scientists need do is, he supposes, seeing the facts. He pictures them, the colorless professionals of science, going off to work in the morning into the universe in a neutral, unexposed state. They then expose themselves like a photographic plate. And then in the darkroom or laboratory they develop the image, so that suddenly and startlingly it appears, printed in capital letters, as a new formula for atomic energy.

Men who have read Balzac and Zola are not deceived by the claims of these writers that they do no more than record the facts. The readers of Christopher Isherwood do not take him literally when he writes: "I am a camera." Yet the same readers solemnly carry with them from their school days this foolish picture of the scientist fixing by some mechanical process the facts of nature. I have had, of all people, a historian tell me that science is a collection of facts, and his voice had not even the irony of one filing cabinet reproving another.

It seems impossible that this historian had ever studied the beginnings of a scientific discovery. The Scientific Revolution can be held to begin in the year 1543 when there was brought to Copernicus, perhaps

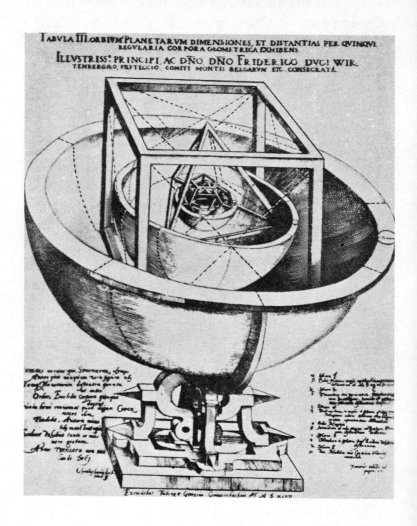

Planetary Orbits Embedded in the Regular Solids.
From Kepler's Mysterium Cosmographicum, 1596

on his deathbed, the first printed copy of the book he had written about a dozen years earlier. The thesis of this book is that the earth moves around the sun. When did Copernicus go out and record this fact with his camera? What appearance in nature prompted his outrageous guess? And in what odd sense is this guess to be called a neutral record of fact?

Less than a hundred years after Copernicus, Kepler published (between 1609 and 1619) the three laws which describe the paths of the planets. The work of Newton and with it most of our mechanics spring from these laws. They have a solid, matter of fact sound. For example, Kepler says that if one squares the year of a planet, one gets a number which is proportional to the cube of its average distance from the sun. Does any one think that such a law is found by taking enough readings and then squaring and cubing everything in sight? If he does then, as a scientist, he is doomed to a wasted life; he has as little prospect of making a scientific discovery as an electronic brain has.

It was not this way that Copernicus and Kepler thought, or that scientists think today. Copernicus found that the orbits of the planets would look simpler if they were looked at from the sun and not from the earth. But he did not in the first place find this by routine calculation. His first step was a leap of imagination—to lift himself from the earth, and put himself wildly, speculatively into the sun. "The earth conceives from the sun," he wrote; and "the sun rules the family of stars." We catch in his mind an image, the gesture of the virile man standing in the sun, with arms outstretched, overlooking the planets. Perhaps Copernicus took the picture from the drawings of the youth with outstretched arms which the Renaissance teachers put into their books on the proportions of the body. Perhaps he knew Leonardo's drawings of his loved pupil Salai. I do not know. To me, the gesture of Copernicus, the shining youth looking outward from the sun, is still vivid in a drawing which William Blake in 1780 based on all these: the drawing which is usually called *Glad Day*.

Kepler's mind, we know, was filled with just such fanciful analogies; and we know what they were. Kepler wanted to relate the speeds of the planets to the musical intervals. He tried to fit the five regular solids into their orbits. None of these likenesses worked, and they have been forgotten; yet they have been and they remain the stepping stones of every creative mind. Kepler felt for his laws by way of metaphors, he searched mystically for likenesses with what he knew in every strange corner of nature. And when among these guesses he hit upon his laws, he did not think of their numbers as the balancing of a cosmic bank account, but as a revelation of the unity in all nature. To us, the analogies by which Kepler listened for the movement of the planets in the music of the spheres are far-fetched; but are they more so than the wild leap by which Rutherford and Bohr found a model for the atom in of all places, the planetary system?

4.

No scientific theory is a collection of facts. It will not even do to call a theory true or false in the simple sense in which every fact is either so or not so. The Epicureans held that matter is made of atoms two thousand years ago and we are now tempted to say that their theory was true. But if we do so, we confuse their notion of matter with our own. John Dalton in 1808 first saw the structure of matter as we do today, and what he took from the ancients was not their theory but something richer, their image: the atom. Much of what was in Dalton's mind was as vague as the Greek notion, and quite as mistaken. But he suddenly gave life to the new facts of chemistry and the ancient theory together, by fusing them to give what neither had: a coherent picture of how matter is linked and built up from different kinds of atoms. The act of fusion is the creative act.

All science is the search for unity in hidden likenesses. The search may be on a grand scale, as in the modern theories which try to link the fields of gravitation and electro-magnetism. But we do not need to be browbeaten by the scale of science. There are discoveries to be made by snatching a small likeness from the air too, if it is bold enough. In 1932 the Japanese physicist Yukawa wrote a paper which can still give heart to a young scientist. He took as his starting point the known fact that waves of light can sometimes behave as if they were separate pellets. From this he reasoned that the forces which hold the nucleus of an atom together might sometimes also be observed as if they were solid pellets. A schoolboy can see how thin Yukawa's analogy is, and his teacher would be severe with it. Yet Yukawa without a blush calculated the mass of the pellet he expected to see, and waited. He was right; his meson was found, and a range of other mesons, neither the existence nor the nature of which had been suspected before. The likeness had borne fruit.

The scientist looks for order in the appearances of nature by exploring such likenesses. For order does not display itself of itself; if it can be said to be there at all, it is not there for the mere looking. There is no way of pointing a finger or a camera at it; order must be discovered and, in a deep sense, it must be created. What we see, as we see it, is mere disorder.

This point has been put trenchantly in a fable by Professor Karl Popper. Suppose that someone wished to give his whole life to science. Suppose that he therefore sat down, pencil in hand, and for the next twenty, thirty, forty years recorded in notebook after notebook everything that he could observe. He may be supposed to leave out nothing: today's humidity, the racing results, the level of cosmic radiation and the stock market prices and the look of Mars, all would be there.

He would have compiled the most careful record of nature that has ever been made; and, dying in the calm certainty of a life well spent, he would of course leave his notebooks to the Royal Society. Would the Royal Society thank him for the treasure of a lifetime of observation? It would not. It would refuse to open his notebooks at all, because it would know without looking that they contain only a jumble of disorderly and meaningless items.

5.

Science finds order and meaning in our experience, and sets about this in quite a different way. It sets about it as Newton did in the story which he himself told in his old age, and of which the schoolbooks give only a caricature. In the year 1665, when Newton was twenty-two, the plague broke out in southern England, and the University of Cambridge was closed. Newton therefore spent the next eighteen months at home, removed from traditional learning, at a time when he was impatient for knowledge and, in his own phrase: "I was in the prime of my age for invention." In this eager, boyish mood, sitting one day in the garden of his widowed mother, he saw an apple fall. So far the books have the story right; we think we even know the kind of apple; tradition has it that it was a Flower of Kent. But now they miss the crux of the story. For what struck the young Newton at the sight was not the thought that the apple must be drawn to the earth by gravity; that conception was older than Newton. What struck him was the conjecture that the same force of gravity, which reaches to the top of the tree, might go on reaching out beyond the earth and its air, endlessly into space. Gravity might reach the moon: this was Newton's new thought; and it might be gravity which holds the moon in her orbit. There and then he calculated what force from the earth would hold the moon, and compared it with the known force of gravity at tree height. The forces agreed; Newton says laconically: "I found them answer pretty nearly." Yet they agreed only nearly: the likeness and the approximation go together, for no likeness is exact. In Newton's sentence modern science is full grown.

It grows from a comparison. It has seized a likeness between two unlike appearances; for the apple in the summer garden and the grave moon overhead are surely as unlike in their movements as two things can be. Newton traced in them two expressions of a single concept, gravitation: and the concept (and the unity) are in that sense his free creation. The progress of science is the discovery at each step of a new order which gives unity to what had long seemed unlike. Faraday did this when he closed the link between electricity and magnetism. Clerk Maxwell did it when he linked both with light. Einstein linked time with space, mass with energy, and the path of light past the sun with the flight of a bullet; and spent his dying years in trying to add to these likenesses another, which

26

would find a single imaginative order between the equations of Cluk Maxwell and his own geometry of gravitation.

When Coleridge tried to define beauty, he returned always to one deep thought: beauty, he said, is "unity in variety." Science is nothing else than the search to discover unity in the wild variety of nature—or more exactly, in the variety of our experience. Poetry, painting, the arts are the same search, in Coleridge's phrase, for unity in variety. Each in its own way looks for likenesses under the variety of human experience. What is a poetic image but the seizing and the exploration of a hidden likeness, in holding together two parts of a comparison which are to give depth each to the other? When Romeo finds Juliet in the tomb, and thinks her dead, he uses in his heartbreaking speech the words:

Death that hath suckt the honey of thy breath.

The critic can only haltingly take to pieces the single shock which this image carries. The young Shakespeare admired Marlowe, and Marlowe's Faustus had said of the ghostly kiss of Helen of Troy that it sucked forth his soul. But that is a pale image; what Shakespeare has done is to fire it with the single word honey. Death is a bee at the lips of Juliet, and the bee is an insect that stings; the sting of death was a commonplace phrase when Shakespeare wrote. The sting is there, under the image; Shakespeare has packed it into the word honey; but the very word rides powerfully over its own undertones. Death is a bee that stings other people, but it comes to Juliet as if she were a flower; this is the moving thought under the instant image. The creative mind speaks in such thoughts.

The poetic image here is also, and accidentally, heightened by the tenderness which town dwellers now feel for country ways. But it need not be; there are likenesses to conjure with, and images as powerful, within the man-made world. The poems of Alexander Pope belong to this world. They are not countrified, and therefore readers today find them unemotional and often artificial. Let me then quote Pope: here he is in a formal satire face to face, towards the end of his life, with his own gifts. In eight lines he looks poignantly forward towards death and back to the laborious years which made him famous.

> Years foll'wing Years, steal something ev'ry day,
> At last they steal us from our selves away;
> In one our Frolicks, one Amusements end,
> In one a Mistress drops, in one a Friend:
> This subtle Thief of Life, this paltry Time,
> What will it leave me, if it snatch my Rhime?
> If ev'ry Wheel of that unweary'd Mill
> That turn'd ten thousand Verses, now stands still.

The human mind had been compared to what the eighteenth century called a mill, that is to a machine, before; Pope's own idol Bolingbroke had compared it to a clockwork. In these lines the likeness goes deeper,

28

for Pope is thinking of the ten thousand verses which he had translated from Homer: what he says is sad and just at the same time, because this really had been a mechanical and at times a grinding task. Yet the clockwork is present in the image too; when the wheels stand still, time for Pope will stand still for ever; we feel that we already hear, over the horizon, the defiance of Faust which Goethe had not yet written—let the clock strike and stop, let the hand fall, and time be at an end.

> *Werd ich zum Augenblicke sagen:*
> *Verweile doch! du bist so schön!*
> *Dann magst du mich in Fesseln schlagen,*
> *Dann will ich gern zugrunde gehn!*
> *Dann mag die Totenglocke schallen,*
> *Dann bist du deines Dienstes frei,*
> *Die Uhr mag stehn, der Zeiger fallen,*
> *Es sei die Zeit für mich vorbei!*

I have quoted Pope and Goethe because their metaphor here is not poetic; it is rather a hand reaching straight into experience and arranging it with new meaning. Metaphors of this kind need not always be written in words. The most powerful of them all is simply the presence of King Lear and his Fool in the hut of a man who is shamming madness, while lightning rages outside. Or let me quote another clash of two conceptions of life, from a modern poet. In his later poems, W. B. Yeats was troubled by the feeling that in shutting himself up to write, he was missing

29

the active pleasures of life; and yet it seemed to him certain that the man who lives for these pleasures will leave no lasting work behind him. He said this at times very simply, too:

> The intellect of man is forced to choose
> Perfection of the life, or of the work.

This problem, whether man fulfills himself in work or in play, is of course more common than Yeats allowed; and it may be more commonplace. But it is given breadth and force by the images in which Yeats pondered it.

> Get all the gold and silver that you can,
> Satisfy ambition, or animate
> The trivial days and ram them with the sun,
> And yet upon these maxims meditate:
> All women dote upon an idle man
> Although their children need a rich estate;
> No man has ever lived that had enough
> Of children's gratitude or woman's love.

The love of women, the gratitude of children: the images fix two philosophies as nothing else can. They are tools of creative thought, as coherent and as exact as the conceptual images with which science works: as time and space, or as the proton and the neutron.

6.

The discoveries of science, the works of art are explorations—more, are explosions, of a hidden likeness. The discoverer or the artist presents in them two aspects of nature and fuses them into one. This is the act of creation, in which an original thought is born, and it is the same act in original science and original art. But it is not therefore the monopoly of the man who wrote the poem or who made the discovery. On the contrary, I believe this view of the creative act to be right because it alone gives a meaning to the act of appreciation. The poem or the discovery exists in two moments of vision: the moment of appreciation as much as that of creation; for the appreciator must see the movement, wake to the echo which was started in the creation of the work. In the moment of appreciation we live again the moment when the creator saw and held the hidden likeness. When a simile takes us aback and persuades us together, when we find a juxtaposition in a picture both odd and intriguing, when a theory is at once fresh and convincing, we do not merely nod over someone else's work. We re-enact the creative act, and we ourselves make the discovery again. At bottom, there is no unifying likeness there until we too have seized it, we too have made it for ourselves.

How slipshod by comparison is the notion that either art or science sets out to copy nature. If the task of the painter were to copy for men what they see, the critic could make only a single judgement: either that the copy is right or that it is wrong. And if science were a copy of fact, then every theory would be either right or wrong, and would be so forever. There would be nothing left for us to say but this is so or is not so. No one who has read a page by a good critic or a speculative scientist can ever again think that this barren choice of yes or no is all that the mind offers.

Reality is not an exhibit for man's inspection, labeled: "Do not touch." There are no appearances to be photographed, no experiences to be copied, in which we do not take part. We re-make nature by the act of discovery, in the poem or in the theorem. And the great poem and the deep theorem are new to every reader, and yet are his own experiences, because he himself re-creates them. They are the marks of unity in variety; and in the instant when the mind seizes this for itself, in art or in science, the heart misses a beat.

2 The
Habit of Truth

1.

IN *The Creative Mind* I set out to show that there exists a single creative activity, which is displayed alike in the arts and in the sciences. It is wrong to think of science as a mechanical record of facts, and it is wrong to think of the arts as remote and private fancies. What makes each human, what makes them universal is the stamp of the creative mind.

I found the act of creation to lie in the discovery of a hidden likeness. The scientist or the artist takes two facts or experiences which are separate; he finds in them a likeness which had not been seen before; and he creates a unity by showing the likeness.

The act of creation is therefore original; but it does not stop with its originator. The work of art or of science is universal because each of us re-creates it. We are moved by the poem, we follow the theorem because in them we discover again and seize the likeness which their creator first seized. The act of appreciation re-enacts the act of creation, and we are (each of us) actors, we are interpreters of it.

35

My examples were drawn from physics and from poetry, because these happen to be the works of man which I know best. But what is great in these is common to all great works. In the museum at Cracow there is a painting by Leonardo da Vinci called "Portrait of a Lady with an Ermine": it shows a girl holding a stoat in her arms. The girl was probably a mistress of Ludovico Sforza, the usurper of Milan, at whose court Leonardo lived from about 1482 to 1499, amid the violence and intrigue which all his life drew him and repelled him together. The stoat was an emblem of Ludovico Sforza, and is probably also a pun on the girl's name. And in a sense the whole picture is a pun, if I may borrow for the word the tragic intensity which Coleridge found in the puns of Shakespeare. Leonardo has matched the stoat in the girl. In the skull under the long brow, in the lucid eyes, in the stately, brutal, beautiful and stupid head of the girl, he has re-discovered the animal nature; and done so without malice, almost as a matter of fact. The very carriage of the girl and the stoat, the gesture of the hand and the claw, explore the character with the anatomy. As we look, the emblematic likeness springs as freshly in our minds as it did in Leonardo's when he looked at the girl and asked her to turn her head. "The Lady with the Ermine" is as much a research into man and animal, and a creation of unity, as is Darwin's *Origin of Species*.

So much may be granted: and yet where is it to stop? The creative act is alike in art and in science; but it cannot be identical in the two; there must be a difference as well as a likeness. For example, the artist in his creation surely has open to him a dimension of freedom which is closed to the scientist. I have insisted that the scientist does not merely record the facts, but he must conform to the facts. The sanction of truth is an exact boundary which encloses him, in a way in which it does not constrain the poet or the painter. Shakespeare can make Romeo say things about the look of Juliet which, although they are revealing, are certainly not true in fact.

O she doth teach the Torches to burne bright.

But soft, what light through yonder window breaks?
It is the East, and Juliet is the Sunne.

And Shakespeare himself is aware that these statements differ from those made by exact observers. For he exploits the difference deliberately for a new poetic effect in the sonnet which begins, tartly:

My Mistres eyes are nothing like the Sunne.

This takes its point and pungency from being unpoetic. Shakespeare designedly in this sonnet plays the finicking scientist straight-faced—

Currall is farre more red, then her lips red,
If snow be white, why then her brests are dun

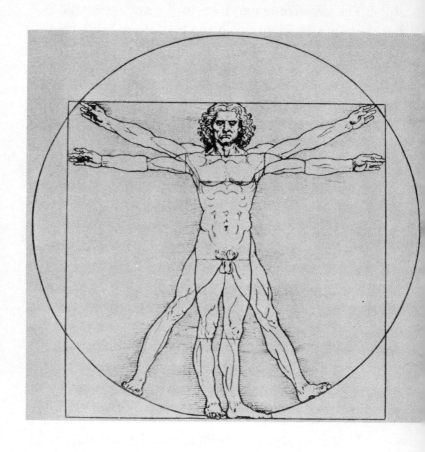

The Proportions of the Human Figure After
Vitruvius *by Leonardo Da Vinci*

—in order to say at last, overwhelmingly, that even in plain fact his love is unbounded. No doubt Shakespeare would have been willing to argue in other places that the poetic image can be called true: the parable of the Prodigal Son is true in some sense, and so is the pursuit of Orestes, and the imagery of *Romeo and Juliet* itself. But the sonnet proves that Shakespeare did not think this meaning of truth to be the same as that which he met in Holinshed's *Chronicles* and William Gilbert's *De Magnete*, and which now dogs the writer of a thesis on electronic networks.

We cannot shirk the historic question, What is truth? On the contrary: the civilization we take pride in took a new strength on the day the question was asked. It took its greatest strength later from Renaissance men like Leonardo, in whom truth to fact became a passion. The sanction of experienced fact as a face of truth is a profound subject, and the mainspring which has moved our civilization since the Renaissance.

2.

Those who have gone out to climb in the Himalayas have brought back, besides the dubious tracks of Abominable Snowmen, a more revealing model of truth. It is contained in the story which they tell of their first sight of some inaccessible and rarely seen mountain. The western climbers, at home with compass and map projection, can match this view of the mountain with another view seen years ago. But to the native climbers with them, each face is a separate picture and puzzle. They may know another face of the mountain, and this face too, better than the stranger; and yet they have no way of fitting the two faces together. Eric Shipton describes this division in the account of his reconnaissance for the new route to Everest, on which the later ascent in 1953 was based. Here is Shipton moving up to a view of Everest from the south which is new to him, but which his leading Sherpa, Angtarkay, had known in childhood.

> Beyond the village of Pangbochi we left the forest behind and entered highland country of heath and coarse grass. We spent the night of the 26th at Phariche, a grazing village then deserted, and on the morning of the 27th we turned into the Lobujya Khola, the valley which contains the Khombu Glacier (which flows from the south and south-west side of Everest). As we climbed into the valley we saw at its head the line of the main watershed. I recognised immediately the peaks and saddles so familiar to us from the Rongbuk (the north) side: Pumori, Lingtren, the Lho La, the North Peak and the west shoulder of Everest. It is curious that Angtarkay, who knew these features as well as I did from the other side and had spent many years of his boyhood grazing yaks in this valley, had never recognised them as the same; nor did he do so now until I pointed them out to him.

It is the inquisitive stranger who points out the mountains which flank Everest. The Sherpa then recognizes the shape of a peak here and of another there. The parts begin to fit together; the puzzled man's mind begins to build a map; and suddenly the pieces are snug, the map will turn around, and the two faces of the mountain are both Everest. Other expeditions in other places have told of the delight of the native climbers at such a recognition.

All acts of recognition are of this kind. The girl met on the beach, the man known long ago, puzzle us for a moment and then fall into place; the new face fits onto and enlarges the old. We are used to make these connections in time; and like the climbers on Everest, we make them also in space. If we did not, our minds would contain only a clutter of isolated experiences. By making such connections we find in our experiences the maps of things.

There is no other evidence for the existence of things. We see the left profile of a man and we see the right profile; we never see them together. What are our grounds for thinking that they belong to one man? What are the grounds for thinking that there is such a thing as the one man at all? By the canons of classical logic, there are no grounds: no one can deduce the man. We infer him from his profiles as we infer that the evening star and the morning star are both the planet Venus: because it makes two experiences cohere, and experience proves it to be consistent. Profiles and full face, back and front, the parts build a round whole, not only by sight but by

the exploration of the touch and the ear, and the
stethoscope and the X-ray tube and all our elabora-
tions of inference. Watch a child's eyes and fingers
together discover that the outside and the inside of
a cup hang together. Watch a man who was born
blind and who can now see, re-building the touched
world by sight; and never again think that the existence of a thing leaps of itself into the mind, immediate and whole. We know the thing only by mapping
and joining our experiences of its aspects.

3.

The discovery of things is made in three steps. At
the first step there are only the separate data of the
senses: we see the head of the penny, we see the tail.
It would be mere pomp to use words as profound as
true and false at this simple step. What we see is
either so or is not so. Where no other judgment can
be made, no more subtle words are in place.

At the second step, we put the head and the tail
together. We see that it makes sense to treat them as
one thing. And the thing is the coherence of its parts
in our experience.

The human mind does not stop there. The animal
can go as far as this: an ape will learn to recognize a
cup whenever and however he sees it, and will know
what to do with it. But all that has been learned
about apes underlines that they find it hard to think
about the cup when it is not in sight, and to imagine

its use then. The human mind has a way of keeping the cup or the penny in mind. This is the third step: to have a symbol or a name for the whole penny. For us the thing has a name, and in a sense is the name: the name or symbol remains present, and the mind works with it, when the thing is absent. By contrast, one of the difficulties which the Sherpas have in seeing Everest is that the mountain goes by different names in different places.

The words true and false have their place at the latter steps, when the data of the senses have been put together to make a thing which is held in the mind. Only then is it meaningful to ask whether what we think about the thing is true. That is, we can now deduce how the thing should behave, and see whether it does so. If this is really one mountain, we say, then the bearing of that landmark should be due east; and we check it. If this is a penny, then it should be sensible to the touch. This is how Macbeth tests the thing he is thinking about and seems to see.

> Is this a Dagger, which I see before me,
> The Handle toward my Hand? Come, let me clutch
> thee—

Macbeth is using the empirical method: the thing is to be tested by its behavior.

> Come, let me clutch thee:
> I haue thee not, and yet I see thee still.
> Art thou not fatall Vision, sensible

43

> *To feeling, as to sight? or art thou but*
> *A Dagger of the Minde, a false Creation?*

"A Dagger of the Minde, a false Creation"; both the word false and the word Creation are exact. What the human mind makes of the sense data, and thinks about, is always a created thing. The construction is true or false by the test of its behavior. We have constructed the thing from the data; we now deduce how the thing should behave; and if it does not, then our construction was false.

4.

I have described so far how we think about things. The view I have put forward also looks beyond things, to the laws and concepts which make up science. This is the real reach of this view: that the three steps by which man constructs and names a mountain are also the steps by which he makes a theory.

Recall the example of the work of Kepler and of Newton; the steps are there to be re-traced. The first step is the collection of data: here, astronomical observations. Next comes the creative step which Kepler took, which finds an order in the data by exploring likenesses. Here the order, the unity is the three laws by which Kepler described the orbit, not of this planet or of that, but simply of a planet.

Kepler's laws, however, put forward no central concept; and the third step is to create this concept. Newton took this step when, at the center of astronomy, he put a single activity of the universe: the concept of gravitation.

There is of course no such thing as gravitation sensible to the touch. It is neither seen nor heard; and if it seems to be felt, this now appears to be a quirk of space. Yet the concept of gravitation was real and true. It was constructed from the data by the same steps which fuse two views of Everest into one mountain or many conversations into one man. And the concept is tested as we test the man, by its behavior: it must be in character. Newton was doing this in his garden in 1666 when he computed the force which holds the moon in her orbit; like Macbeth, he was testing the creation of the mind.

The creation was a concept—a connected set of concepts. There was the concept of a universal gravitation, reaching beyond the tree tops and the air to the ends of space. There was the concept of other universal forces in space which try to pull the moon away as a whirling stone pulls away from its string. And there was the concept which put an end to the four elements of Aristotle: the concept of mass, alike in the apple and the earth and the moon, in all earthly and all heavenly bodies.

All these are real creations: they find a unity in what seemed unlike. They are symbols; they do not exist without the creation. Solid as it seems, there is no such thing as mass; as Newton ruefully found, it

45

cannot be defined. We experience mass only as the behavior of bodies, and it is a single concept only because they behave consistently.

Indeed, the concept of mass is a peculiarly apt example. For in the physics of Newton, there are two concepts of mass, which are distinct. One is the inertial mass of a body—that which must be overcome when it is thrown. The other is the gravitational mass of the same body—that which must be overcome when it is lifted from the ground. Newton knew, of course, that the inertial mass is equal to the gravitational mass; but why are they equal, why should they be the same single mass? This is a question which Einstein asked; and in order to answer it, he built in 1915 the whole theory of General Relativity. Only in that theory were the two faces of mass made one, and made the unity which is the single concept, mass.

This sequence is characteristic of science. It begins with a set of appearances. It organizes these into laws. And at the center of the laws it finds a knot, a point at which several laws cross: a symbol which gives unity to the laws themselves. Mass, time, magnetic moment, the unconscious: we have grown up with these symbolic concepts, so that we are startled to be told that man had once to create them for himself. He had indeed, and he has; for mass is not an intuition in the muscle, and time is not bought ready-made at the watchmaker's.

And we test the concept, as we test the thing, by

its implications. That is, when the concept has been built up from some experiences, we reason what behavior in other experiences should logically flow from it. If we find this behavior, we go on holding the concept as it is. If we do not find the behavior which the concept logically implies, then we must go back and correct it. In this way logic and experiment are locked together in the scientific method, in a constant to and fro in which each follows the other.

5.

This view of the scientific method is not shared by all those who have thought about it. There are two schools of philosophy which are suspicious of conceptual thinking and want to replace it wholly by the manipulation of facts. One is that offshoot of the English empiricist tradition which goes through Bertrand Russell to Wittgenstein and the logical positivists. This school holds that a rigorous description of all nature can be pieced together, like a gigantic tinkertoy, out of small units of fact, each of which can be separately verified to be so. The other is the school founded by Ernst Mach in Austria, and led more recently by Perey Bridgman in America, which holds that science is strictly an account of operations and their results. This behaviorist school would like to discard all models of nature, and confine itself always to saying that if we do *this*, we get a larger measurement than if we do *that*.

These accounts of science seem to me mistaken, on two counts. First, they fly in the face of the historical evidence. Since Greek times and before, lucid thinkers and indeed all men have used such words as space and mass and light. They have not asked either Russell's or Bridgman's leave, yet what they have done with the words belongs to the glories of science as well as philosophy; and it is late in the day to forbid them this language.

And second, both schools fly in the face of the contemporary evidence. We have good grounds to believe, from studies of animals and men, that thinking as we understand it is made possible only by the use of names or symbols. Other animals than man have languages, in Bridgman's sense; for example, bees signal to one another where to go in order to find nectar. Bernard de Mandeville, who wrote *The Fable of the Bees* in an eighteenth-century parable, would have thought this the height of rational behaviour. But no active scientist sees it so, because he knows that science is not something which insects or machines can do. What makes it different is a creative process, the exploration of likenesses; and this has sadly tiptoed out of the mechanical worlds of the positivists and the operationalists, and left them empty.

The world which the human mind knows and explores does not survive if it is emptied of thought. And thought does not survive without symbolic concepts. The symbol and the metaphor are as necessary to science as to poetry. We are as helpless today to define mass, fundamentally, as Newton was. But we do not therefore think, and neither did he, that the equations which contain mass as an unknown are mere rules of thumb. If we had been content with that view, we should never have learned to turn mass into energy. In forming a concept of mass, in speaking the word, we begin a process of experiment and correction which is the creative search for truth.

In the village in which I live there is a pleasant doctor who is a little deaf. He is not shy about it and he wears a hearing aid. My young daughter has known him and his aid since she was a baby. When at the age of two she first met another man who was wearing a hearing aid, she simply said: "That man is a doctor." Of course she was mistaken. Yet if both men had worn not hearing aids but stethoscopes, we should have been delighted by her generalization. Even then she would have had little idea of what a doctor does, and less of what he is. But she would have been then, and to me she was even while she was mistaken, on the path to human knowledge which goes by way of the making and correcting of concepts.

6.

I should be unjust if I did not grant that the positivist and operational schools of philosophy have had reason to be wary of the appeal to concepts. Russell and Bridgman shied away from the concept because it has a bad record, which still befuddles its use. Historically, concepts have commonly been set up as absolute and inborn notions, like the space and time which Kant believed to be ready-made in the mind. The view that our concepts are built up from experience and have constantly to be tested and corrected in experience, is not classical. The classical view has been that concepts are not accessible to empirical tests. How many people understand, even today, that the concepts of science are neither absolute nor everlasting? And beyond the field of science, in society, in personality, above all in ethics, how many people will allow the sanction of experienced fact? The common view remains the classical view, that the concepts of value—justice and honor, dignity and tolerance—have an inwardness which is inaccessible to experience.

The roots of this error go down into the closed logic of the Middle Ages. The characteristic and distinguished example is the method of St. Thomas Aquinas. The physics which was current for three centuries before the Scientific Revolution derived from Aristotle by way of Arab scholars, and had been formed into a system by Aquinas. But it did not share the test of truth of modern physics. Between the years 1256 and 1259, Aquinas held about 250 discussion classes, all on the subject of truth. Each class lasted two days. The questions discussed belong to a world of discourse which simply has no common frontier with ours. They are such questions as: "Is God's knowledge the cause

of things?" "Is the Book of Life the same as predesti-
nation?" "Do angels know the future?"

I do not dismiss these as merely fanciful questions,
any more than I regard *Tamburlaine* and *The Mar-
riage of Heaven and Hell* as fantasies. Yet it is plain
that they have no bearing on matters of truth and
falsehood as we understand them, inductively. These
debates are scholastic exercises in absolute logic. They
begin from concepts which are held to be fixed abso-
lutely; they then proceed by deduction; and what is
found in this way is subject to no further test. The
deductions are true because the first concepts were
true: that is the scholastic system. It is also the logic
of Aristotle. Unhappily, it makes poor physics, for
there the gap between the intuitive and the corrected
concept is gaping.

7.

Modern science also began by hankering after
purely deductive systems. Its first model, of course,
was Euclid. One of its historic moments was the con-
version of Thomas Hobbes, some time between 1629
and 1631.

He was 40 yeares old before he looked on geometry;
which happened accidentally. Being in a gentleman's
library Euclid's Elements lay open, and 'twas the 47
El. libri I. He read the proposition. 'By G—,' sayd he,
(He would now and then sweare, by way of emphasis)
'By G—,' sayd he, 'this is impossible!' So he reads the

demonstration of it, which referred him back to such a proposition; which proposition he read. That referred him back to another, which he also read. *Et sic deinceps*, that at last he was demonstratively convinced of that trueth. This made him in love with geometry.

This account was written by John Aubrey, who was Hobbes' friend. Aubrey of course assumes that everyone knows which is the 47th proposition in the first book of Euclid; if we do not, we miss the explosive charge in the story. For the 47th proposition is the theorem of Pythagoras about the squares on the sides of a right-angled triangle—the most famous theorem of antiquity, for which Pythagoras is said to have sacrificed a hundred oxen to the Muses in thanks. Hobbes, in an age which knew the theorems by their numbers, at forty did not know the content of this; and when he learned it, it changed his life.

From then on, Hobbes became a pioneer of the deductive method in science. In his time, his innovation was necessary; but soon the movement of science left it behind. For when Hobbes took over the deductive method, he took also Euclid's notion that we know intuitively what points are, what an angle is, what we mean by parallel. The concepts and the axioms were supposed to be simply self-evident, in geometry or in the physical world.

Science has not stopped there since Hobbes, but such subjects as ethics have. In Hobbes' lifetime, Spinoza presented his *Ethics, ordine geometrico dem-*

onstrate, proved in geometrical order. The book begins in the Euclidean manner with eight definitions and seven axioms. This is a modest apparatus with which to attack the universe, for even Euclid's geometry of the plane needs more than twenty axioms. But Spinoza tackles it bravely and indeed profoundly, and it is not his fault that after a time we come to feel that we are standing still. The geometrical system of ethics has exhausted its discoveries. It no longer says anything new; and worse, it can learn nothing new.

Here is the heart of the difference between the two ways in which we order our lives. Both ways hinge on central concepts. In both we reason from the central concepts to the consequences which flow from them. But here the two ways divide. In the field of ethics, of conduct and of values, we think as Aquinas and Spinoza thought: that our concepts must remain unchangeable because they are either inspired or self-evident. In the field of science, four hundred years of adventure have taught us that the rational method is more subtle than this, and that concepts are its most subtle creations. A hundred and fifty years ago, Gauss and others proved that the axioms of Euclid are neither self-evident nor necessarily exact in our world. Much of physics since then, for instance in relativity, has been the re-making of a more delicate and a more exciting concept of space. The need to do so has sprung from the facts; and yet, how the new concepts have outraged our self-evident notions of how a well-

mannered space *ought* to behave! Quantum mechanics
has been a constant scandal because it has said that
the world of the small scale does not behave entirely
like a copy of the man-sized world. Swift in *Gulliver's
Travels* had remarked something like this back in
1726, and it ought no longer to shock us; but of
course, Swift was a scandal, too, in his day.

Is it true that the concepts of science and those of
ethics and values belong to different worlds? Is the
world of *what is* subject to test, and is the world of
what ought to be subject to no test? I do not believe
so. Such concepts as justice, humanity and the full life
have not remained fixed in the last four hundred years,
whatever churchmen and philosophers may pretend.
In their modern sense, they did not exist when Aquinas
wrote; they do not exist now in civilizations which dis-
regard the physical fact. And here I do not mean only
the scientific fact. The tradition of the Renaissance is
of a piece, in art and in science, in believing that the
physical world is a source of knowledge. The poet as
much as the biologist now believes that life speaks to
him through the senses. But this was not always so:
Paolo Veronese was reproved by the Inquisition in
1573 for putting the real world into a sacred painting.
And it is not so everywhere now: the ancient civilizations of the East still reject the senses as a source of
knowledge, and this is as patent in their formal poetry
and their passionless painting as in their science.

By contrast, the sanction of experienced fact has

changed and shaped all the concepts of men who have felt the Scientific Revolution. A civilization cannot hold its activities apart, or put on science like a suit of clothes—a workday suit which is not good enough for Sunday. The study of perspective in the Renaissance chimes with the rise of sensuous painting. And the distaste of painters for naturalism for fifty years now is surely related to the new structure which scientists have struggled to find in nature in the same time. A civilization is bound up with one way of experiencing life. And ours can no more keep its concepts than its wars apart in pigeonholes.

All this is plain once it is seen that science also is a system of concepts: the place of experience is to test and correct the concept. The test is: Will the concept work? Does it give an unforced unity to the experience of men? Does the concept make life orderly, not by edict but in fact?

Men have insisted on carrying this test into the systems of society and of conduct. What else cost Charles I his head in 1649? And what brought Charles II back in 1660, yet at last exiled his family for Dutchmen and Germans? Not the high talk about the divine right of kings, and not the Bill of Rights, but their test in experience. England would have been willing to live by either concept, as it has been willing to live by Newton or by Einstein: it chose the one which made society work of itself, without constraint.

Since then society has evolved a sequence of central

concepts each of which was at one time thought to make it work of itself, and each of which has had to be corrected to the next. There was the early eighteenth-century concept of self-interest, in Mandeville and others; then came enlightened self-interest; then the greatest happiness of the greatest number; utility; the labor theory of value; and thence its expression either in the welfare state or in the classless society. Men have never treated any one of these concepts as the last, and they do not mean to do so now. What has driven them, what drives them is the refusal to acknowledge the concept as either an edict or self-evident. Does this really work, they ask, without force, without corruption and without another arbitrary superstructure of laws which do not derive from the central concept. Do its consequences fit our experience; do men in such a society live so or not so? This is the simple but profound test of fact by which we have come to judge the large words of the makers of states and systems. We see it cogently in the Declaration of Independence, which begins in the round Euclidean manner: "We hold these truths to be self-evident," but which takes the justification for its action at last from "a long train of abuses and usurpations": the colonial system had failed to make a workable society.

8.

One example among others points the modern lesson. When Warren Hastings was impeached in 1786

for his high-handed rule in India, ho had two griev-
ances on his side. One was that the violence and corruption of which he was accused were in any case
commonplace throughout Indian society then. The
other was that some of his accusers (and chiefly
Burke) were not free from a corrupt interest in Indian
affairs themselves. Warren Hastings was acquitted,
but not on these grounds, for they missed the difference between India then and Europe. Man as man had
a different value in the two continents. The Renaissance had made the difference; and England with her
dissenters had been evolving the new value for two
hundred years, always by the downright test of making
a stable and self-correcting society. The conduct of
Warren Hastings was to be judged by the same aim,
and by no other; the standards of lesser societies ruled
by conquerors, the motives of lesser men had no bearing on it.

The cultures of the East still differ from ours as
they did then. They still belittle man as individual
man. Under this runs an indifference to the world of
the senses, of which the indifference to experienced
fact is one face. Anyone who has worked in the East
knows how hard it is there to get an answer to a question of fact. When I had to study the casualties from
the atomic bombs in Japan at the end of the war, I
was dogged and perplexed by this difficulty. The man
I asked, whatever man one asks, does not really understand what one wants to know: or rather, he does not

understand that one wants to know. He wants to do what is fitting, he is not unwilling to be candid, but at bottom he does not know the facts because they are not his language. These cultures of the East have remained fixed because they lack the language and the very habit of fact.

To us, the habit of simple truth to experience has been the mover of civilization. The last war showed starkly what happens to our societies and to us as men when this habit is broken. The occupation of France forced on the people of France a split in the conduct of each man: a code of truth to his fellows, and a code of deceit to the conquerors. This was a heroic division, more difficult to sustain than we can know and for which the world has still to thank Frenchmen. Yet those who lived in that division will never wholly recover from it, and the habits of distrust and withdrawal which it created will long hamstring the free life of France and of Europe.

This is the grave indictment of every state in which men are cautious of speaking out to any man they meet. The decay of the habit of truth is damaging to those who must fear to speak. But how much more destructive, how degrading it is to the loud-mouthed conquerors. The people whom their conquests really sapped were the Nazis themselves. Picture the state of German thought when Werner Heisenberg was criticized by the S.S., and had to ask Himmler to support his scientific standing. Heisenberg had won the

Nobel prize at the age of thirty; his principle of un-
certainty is one of the two or three deep concepts
which science has found in this century; and he was
trying to warn Germans that they must not dismiss
such discoveries as relativity because they disliked the
author. Yet Himmler, who had been a schoolmaster,
took months of petty inquiry (someone in his family
knew Heisenberg) before he authorized, of all people,
Heydrich to protect Heisenberg. His letter to Heydrich is a paper monument to what happens to the
creative mind in a society without truth. For Himmler
writes that he has heard that Heisenberg is good
enough to be earmarked later for his own Academy for
Welteislehre. This was an Academy which Himmler
proposed to devote to the conviction which he either
shared with or imposed on his scientific yes-men, that
the stars are made of ice.

This nonsense of course is like the nonsense that
Germans were taught to credit about the human races.
The state of mind, the state of society is of a piece.
When we discard the test of fact in what a star is, we
discard it in what a man is. A society holds together
by the respect which man gives to man; it fails in fact,
it falls apart into groups of fear and power, when its
concept of man is false. We find the drive which
makes a society stable at last in the search for what
makes us men. This is a search which never ends: to
end it is to freeze the concept of man in a caricature
beyond correction, as the societies of caste and master-

race have done. In the knowledge of man as in that of
nature, the habit of truth to experienced fact will not
let our concepts alone. This is what destroyed the
empires of Himmler and of Warren Hastings. When
Hastings stood his trial, William Wilberforce was
rousing England to put an end to the trade in slaves.
He had at bottom only one ground: that dark men are
men. A century and more of scientific habit by then
had made his fellows find that true, and find Hastings
not so much a tyrant as a cheat.

9.

There have always been two ways of looking for
truth. One is to find concepts which are beyond challenge, because they are held by faith or by authority
or the conviction that they are self-evident. This is the
mystic submission to truth which the East has chosen
and which dominated the axiomatic thought of the
scholars of the Middle Ages. So St. Thomas Aquinas
holds that faith is a higher guide to truth than knowledge is: the master of medieval science puts science
firmly into second place.

But long before Aquinas wrote, Peter Abelard had
already challenged the whole notion that there are
concepts which can only be felt by faith or authority.
All truth, even the highest, is accessible to test, said
Abelard: "By doubting we are led to enquire, and by
enquiry we perceive the truth." The words might have
been written five hundred years later by Descartes and

could have been a recipe for the Scientific Revolution. We have the same dissent from authority in the Reformation; for in effect what Luther said in 1517 was that we may appeal to a demonstrable work of God, the Bible, to override any established authority. The Scientific Revolution begins when Copernicus put forward the bolder proposition that there is another work of God to which we may appeal even beyond this: the great work of nature. No absolute statement is allowed to be out of reach of the test, that its consequence must conform to the facts of nature.

The habit of testing and correcting the concept by its consequences in experience has been the spring within the movement of our civilization ever since. In science and in art and in self-knowledge we explore and move constantly by turning to the world of sense to ask, Is this so? This is the habit of truth, always minute yet always urgent, which for four hundred years has entered every action of ours; and has made our society and the value it sets on man, as surely as it has made the linotype machine and the scout knife and *King Lear* and the *Origin of Species* and Leonardo's "Lady with the Ermine."

3 The Sense of
Human Dignity

1.

THE subject of this book is the evolution of contemporary values. My theme is that the values which we accept today as permanent and often as self-evident have grown out of the Renaissance and the Scientific Revolution. The arts and the sciences have changed the values of the Middle Ages; and this change has been an enrichment, moving towards what makes us more deeply human.

This theme plainly outrages a widely held view of what science does. If, as many think, science only compiles an endless dictionary of facts, then it must be neutral (and neuter) as a machine is; it cannot bear on human values. But of course science is not a giant dictionary, any more than literature is; both are served by, they do not serve, the makers of their dictionaries. *The Creative Mind* had this strenuous task, to show that science is a creative activity. In the act of creation, a man brings together two facets of reality and, by discovering a likeness between them, suddenly makes them one. This act is the same in Leonardo, in Keats and in Einstein. And the spectator who is moved by the finished work of art or the scientific theory re-lives the same discovery; his appreciation also is a re-creation.

Yet when it has been granted that science and art both find hidden likenesses and order in what seemed unlike, there remains a doubt. Is there not this difference between them, that the likenesses which a science finds have to conform to a sanction of fact from which the arts are free? Must not science be true?

The Habit of Truth asked the historic question, What is truth? I set out, of course, to distinguish what is true, less from what is simply false (which seldom puzzles us) than from what is illusory: the hallucination of an ill-grounded or a disordered belief. My method derived from the tradition of pragmatism which, since William James advanced it about 1890 (and Charles Peirce before that), has been the most original philosophical thought in America. It took for its model of truth the reality of things. How do we come to believe that there is such a thing as Everest? For we do not see the thing in itself; only an aspect or an effect of it reaches us. Yet we recognize the thing as one, because this gives order to its aspects; the thing makes a unity of the different effects by which it enters our world.

I do not think that truth becomes more primitive if we pursue it to simpler facts. For no fact in the world is instant, infinitesimal and ultimate, a single mark.

There are, I hold, no atomic facts; in the language of science, every fact is a field.

Truth in science is like Everest, an ordering of the facts. We organize our experience in patterns which, formalized, make the network of scientific laws. But science does not stop at the formulation of laws; we none of us do, and none of us, in public with his work or in private with his conscience, lives by following a schedule of laws. We condense the laws around concepts. So science takes its coherence, its intellectual and imaginative strength together, from the concepts at which its laws cross, like knots in a mesh. Gravitation, mass and energy, evolution, enzymes, the unconscious—these are the bold creations of science, the strong invisible skeleton on which it articulates the movements of the world.

Science is indeed a truthful activity. And whether we look at facts, at things or at concepts, we cannot disentangle truth from meaning—that is, from an inner order. Truth therefore is not different in science and in the arts; the facts of the heart, the bases of personality, are merely more difficult to communicate. Truth to fact is the same habit in both and has the same importance for both, because facts are the only raw material from which we can derive a change of mind. In science, the appeal to fact is the exploration of the concept in its logical consequences. In the arts, the emotional facts fix the limits of experience which can be shared in their language.

I have recalled the apparatus which I have previously set up in order that I may now use it to examine the values by which we live. Some people think that these values are inborn as the sense of sight is, and they treat any heresy as an affliction which the sufferer would not have contracted had his habits been cleaner. Others accept the notions of value as absolute edicts which we must indeed learn, and if possible learn to like, but which we cannot usefully question. These people are all anxious that we shall behave well and yet that we shall not question how we behave. Because they believe that there is no rational foundation for values, they fear that an appeal to logic can lead only first to irreverence and then to hedonism.

I do not share this fear, and I do not need it to sustain my sense of values. To me, such a concept as duty is like the concept of mass. I was not born with a concept of mass, and I did not receive it by edict; yet both my inborn senses and my education took part in the process of elucidating it as it grew out of my experience and that of others. I do not find it difficult to defend my concept of mass on these grounds, and I see no reason why I should base the concept of duty as a value on different grounds.

There is I think another fear that moves people to resist the suggestion that the values by which they live should be studied empirically. They grant that this study may indeed reveal what men do in order to prosper; but is this, they ask, what they ought to do?

Is it not more often precisely what they ought not to do? Surely, say the righteous, it is the wicked who flourish, and they flourish because they practice what is wicked. So that if social science studies, as natural science does, what works and what does not, the laws which it traces are likely, they fear, to be very unsavory.

I doubt whether this dark view will bear the light of history. Is it really true that the wicked prosper? In the convulsions of nations, have tyrannies outlived their meeker rivals? Rome has not survived the Christian martyrs. Machiavelli in *The Prince* was impressed by the triumphs of the Borgias, and he has impressed us; but were they in fact either successful or enviable? Was the fate of Hitler and Mussolini better? And even in the short perspective of our own street, do we really find that the cheats have the best of it? Or are we merely yielding to the comforting belief that, because one of our neighbors flourishes, he is *ipso facto* wicked?

There is a grave error in this fear that the study of society must reveal a moral form of Gresham's law, that the bad drives out the good. The error is to suppose that the norms of conduct in a society might remain fixed while the conduct of its members changes. This is not so. A society cannot remain lawful when many members break the laws. In an orderly society, an impostor now and again gains an advantage; but he gains it only so long as imposture remains occasional—so long, that is, as his own practice does not destroy the social order. The counterfeiter can exploit the confidence of society in the value of money only so long as he himself does not sap this confidence. Destroy this, and Gresham's law really takes its revenge; the society falls apart to suspicion and barter.

If we are to study conduct, we must follow it in both directions: into the duties of men, which alone hold a society together, and also into the freedom to act personally which the society must still allow its men. The problem of values arises only when men try to fit together their need to be social animals with their need to be free men. There is no problem, and there are no values, until men want to do both. If an anarchist wants only freedom, whatever the cost, he will prefer the jungle of man at war with man. And if a tyrant wants only social order, he will create the totalitarian state. He will single out those who question or dissent—those whom Plato in the *Republic* called poets and in the *Laws* called materialists, and whom Congressional Committees more simply call scientists; and he will have them, as Plato advised, exiled, or *gleichgeschaltet* or liquidated or investigated.

2.

The concepts of value are profound and difficult exactly because they do two things at once: they join men into societies, and yet they preserve for them a freedom which makes them single men. A philosophy which does not acknowledge both needs cannot evolve values and indeed cannot allow them. This is true of a wholly social philosophy such as dialectical material-ism, in which the community lays down how the indi-vidual must act; there is no room for him to ask him-self how he *ought* to act. And it is equally true of the individualist systems which have for some time had a following in England—systems such as logical positiv-ism and its modern derivative, analytical philosophy.

It is relevant to examine these last philosophies be-cause they make a special claim to be scientific. In their reaction against the metaphysics of the nine-teenth century, they have returned to the empiricist tradition which goes back in British philosophy to Thomas Hobbes, to John Locke, and above all to David Hume. This is a tradition which looks for the material and the tests of a philosophy in the physical world; the evidence which it seeks is, roughly, that which a scientist seeks, and it rejects evidence which would not pass muster in science. Those who led the return to the empiricist tradition, first Bertrand Russell and then Ludwig Wittgenstein, were in fact trained in scientific disciplines.

In his early writing, Wittgenstein held that a state-ment makes sense only if it can be tested in the physi-cal world. In his later writing, Wittgenstein came to look for the meaning of a statement in the way in which it can be used: the contexts and the intentions into which it fits. That is, his early view of truth was positivist, and his later view was analytical. Wittgenstein's followers have now enthroned his later analysis of usage into a philosophical method which often seems remote from any universal test, but their aim remains, as it was his, to make our understanding of the world tally with the way in which it works in fact.

Positivists and analysts alike believe that the words *is* and *ought* belong to different worlds, ·so that sentences which are constructed with *is* usually have a verifiable meaning, but sentences constructed with *ought* never have. This is because Wittgenstein's unit, and Russell's unit, is one man; all British empiricist philosophy is individualist. And it is of course clear that if the only criterion of true and false which a man accepts is that man's, then he has no base for social agreement. The question how a man *ought* to behave is a social question, which always involves several people; and if he accepts no evidence and no judgment except his own, he has no tools with which to frame an answer.

The issue then is, whether verification can be accepted as a principle if it is assumed to be carried out by one man. This is as factual an issue as that which faced physics in 1905. Einstein did not debate in 1905 whether space and time may be absolute, in principle; he asked how physicists in fact measure them. So it is irrelevant (and metaphysical) to debate whether verification can be absolute, in principle; the question is, how do men in fact verify a statement? How do they confirm or challenge the assertion, for example, that "the Crab nebula is the dust of a supernova which exploded in 1054, and it glows because some of it is radioactive carbon which was made in the supernova."

This is a fairly simple speculation, as science goes. The positivist would break it into still simpler pieces, and would then propose to verify each. But it is an illusion, and a fatal illusion, to think that he could verify them himself. Even in principle, he could not verify the historical part of this statement without searching the records of others and believing them. And in practice, he could not verify the rate of expansion of the Crab nebula and the processes which might cause it to glow without the help of a sequence of instrument makers and astronomers and nuclear physicists, specialists in this and that, each of whom he must trust and believe. All this knowledge, all our knowledge, has been built up communally; there would be no astrophysics, there would be no history, there would not even be language, if man were a solitary animal.

The fallacy which imprisons the positivist and the analyst is the assumption that he can test what is true and false unaided. This of course prevents him from making any social judgment. Suppose then that we give up this assumption and acknowledge that, even in the verification of facts, we need the help of others. What follows?

It follows that we must be able to rely on other

people; we must be able to trust their word. That is, it follows that there is a principle which binds society together, because without it the individual would be helpless to tell the true from the false. This principle is truthfulness. If we accept truth as an individual criterion, then we have also to make it the cement to hold society together.

The positivist holds that only those statements have meaning which can in principle be verified and found to be so or not so. Statements which contain the word *is* can be of this kind; statements which contain the word *ought* cannot. But we now see that, underlying this criterion, there is a social nexus which alone makes verification possible. This nexus is held together by the obligation to tell the truth. Thus it follows that there is a social injunction implied in the positivist and analyst method. This social axiom is that

We OUGHT *to act in such a way that what* IS *true can be verified to be so.*

This is the light by which the working of society is to be examined. And in order to keep the study in a manageable field, I will continue to choose a society in which the principle of truth rules. Therefore the society which I will examine is that formed by scientists themselves: it is the body of scientists.

It may seem strange to call this a society, and yet it is an obvious choice; for having said so much about the working of science, I should be shirking all our unspoken questions if I did not ask how scientists work together. The dizzy progress of science, theoretical and practical, has depended on the existence of a fellowship of scientists which is free, uninhibited and communicative. It is not an upstart society, for it derives its traditions, both of scholarship and of service, from roots which reach through the Renaissance into the monastic communities and the first universities. The men and women who practice the sciences make a company of scholars which has been more lasting than any modern state, yet which has changed and evolved as no church has. What power holds them together?

In an obvious sense, theirs is the power of virtue. By the worldly standards of public life, all scholars in their work are of course oddly virtuous. They do not make wild claims, they do not cheat, they do not try to persuade at any cost, they appeal neither to prejudice nor to authority, they are often frank about their ignorance, their disputes are fairly decorous, they do not confuse what is being argued with race, politics, sex or age, they listen patiently to the young and to the old who both know everything. These are the general virtues of scholarship, and they are peculiarly the virtues of science. Individually, scientists no doubt have human weaknesses. Several of them may have mistresses or read Karl Marx; some of them may even be homosexuals and read Plato. But in a world in which state and dogma seem always either to threaten or to cajole, the body of scientists is trained to avoid and organized to resist every form of persuasion but the fact. A scientist who breaks this rule, as Lysenko has done, is ignored. A scientist who finds that the rule has been broken in his laboratory, as Kammerer found, kills himself.

I have already implied that I do not trace these virtues to any personal goodness in scientists. A recent study has indeed shown that, as a profession, science attracts men whose temperament is grave, awkward and absorbed. But this is in the main the scholar's temperament, which is shared by historians and literary critics and painters in miniature. For all their private virtues, these men form today what they formed four hundred years ago, scattered collections of individuals. It is not their temperament which has made of scientists so steadfast and so powerful a society.

Nor is it the profession of science, simply as a profession. Every profession has its solemn codes: the lawyers and the salesmen, the accountants and the musicians and the consulting engineers. When a member of these combinations behaves outrageously, he is expelled. But this association is as circumspect as a licensing board and as formal as a Trade Union. It guides and it protects the practitioner, it offers him models and friends, and it gives a personality to his work. It can be as far-reaching as the Hippocratic Oath or the ceremonial of Freemasonry. And yet we have only to see how much alike are all these codes, how pious and how general, to know at once that they do not spring from the pith and sap of the work which they regulate. They are not thrust up, a sharp green bough, from the ruling passion of their adherents. It is the other way about: their codes are a reminder to each profession that the sanctions of society at large reach into them also. Our civilization has imposed itself on these professions; but no one claims that it has imposed itself on science.

3.

The values of science derive neither from the virtues of its members, nor from the finger-wagging codes of conduct by which every profession reminds itself to be good. They have grown out of the practice of science, because they are the inescapable conditions for its practice.

Science is the creation of concepts and their exploration in the facts. It has no other test of the concept than its empirical truth to fact. Truth is the drive at the center of science; it must have the habit of truth, not as a dogma but as a process. Consider then, step by step, what kind of society scientists have been compelled to form in this single pursuit. If truth is to be found, not given, and if therefore it is to be tested in action, what other conditions (and with them, what other values) grow of themselves from this?

First, of course, comes independence, in observation and thence in thought. I once told an audience of school children that the world would never change if they did not contradict their elders. I was chagrined to find next morning that this axiom outraged their parents. Yet it is the basis of the scientific method. A man must see, do and think things for himself, in the face of those who are sure that they have already been over all that ground. In science, there is no substitute for independence.

It has been a by-product of this that, by degrees, men have come to give a value to the new and the bold in all their work. It was not always so. European thought and art before the Renaissance were happy in the faith that there is nothing new under the sun. John Dryden in the seventeenth century, and Jonathan Swift as it turned into the eighteenth, were still fighting Battles of the Books to prove that no modern work could hope to rival the classics. They were not over-powered by argument or example (not even by their own examples), but by the mounting scientific tradition among their friends in the new Royal Society. Today we find it as natural to prize originality in a child's drawing and an arrangement of flowers as in an invention. Science has bred the love of originality as a mark of independence.

Independence, originality, and therefore dissent: these words show the progress, they stamp the character of our civilization as once they did that of Athens in flower. From Luther in 1517 to Spinoza grinding lenses, from Huguenot weavers and Quaker ironmas-

ters to the Puritans founding Harvard, and from Newton's heresies to the calculated universe of Eddington,
the profound movements of history have been begun
by unconforming men. Dissent is the native activity of
the scientist, and it has got him into a good deal of
trouble in the last years. But if that is cut off, what is
left will not be a scientist. And I doubt whether it will
be a man. For dissent is also native in any society
which is still growing. Has there ever been a society
which has died of dissent? Several have died of con-
formity in our lifetime.

Dissent is not itself an end; it is the surface mark
of a deeper value. Dissent is the mark of freedom, as
originality is the mark of independence of mind. And
as originality and independence are private needs for
the existence of a science, so dissent and freedom are
its public needs. No one can be a scientist, even in
private, if he does not have independence of observation and of thought. But if in addition science is to
become effective as a public practice, it must go
further; it must protect independence. The safeguards
which it must offer are patent: free inquiry, free
thought, free speech, tolerance. These values are so
familiar to us, yawning our way through political
perorations, that they seem self-evident. But they are
self-evident, that is, they are logical needs, only where
men are committed to explore the truth: in a scientific
society. These freedoms of tolerance have never been
notable in a dogmatic society, even when the dogma

was Christian. They have been granted only when scientific thought flourished once before, in the youth of Greece.

4.

I have been developing an ethic for science which derives directly from its own activity. It might have seemed at the outset that this study could lead only to a set of technical rules: to elementary rules for using test tubes or sophisticated rules for inductive reasoning. But the inquiry turns out quite otherwise. There are, oddly, no technical rules for success in science. There are no rules even for using test tubes which the brilliant experimenter does not flout; and alas, there are no rules at all for making successful general inductions. This is not where the study of scientific practice leads us. Instead, the conditions for the practice of science are found to be of another and an unexpected kind. Independence and originality, dissent and freedom and tolerance: such are the first needs of science; and these are the values which, of itself, it demands and forms.

The society of scientists must be a democracy. It can keep alive and grow only by a constant tension between dissent and respect, between independence from the views of others and tolerance for them. The crux of the ethical problem is to fuse these, the private and the public needs. Tolerance alone is not enough; this is why the bland, kindly civilizations of the East, where to contradict is a personal affront, developed no strong science. And independence is not enough either: the sad history of genetics, still torn today by the quarrels of sixty years ago, shows that. Every scientist has to learn the hard lesson, to respect the views of the next man—even when the next man is tactless enough to express them.

Tolerance among scientists cannot be based on indifference, it must be based on respect. Respect as a personal value implies, in any society, the public acknowledgements of justice and of due honor. These are values which to the layman seem most remote from any abstract study. Justice, honor, the respect of man for man: What, he asks, have these human values to do with science? The question is a foolish survival of those nineteenth-century quarrels which always came back to equate ethics with the Book of Genesis. If critics in the past had ever looked practically to see how a science develops, they would not have asked such a question. Science confronts the work of one man with that of another and grafts each on each; and it cannot survive without justice and honor and respect between man and man. Only by these means can science pursue its steadfast object, to explore truth. If these values did not exist, then the society of scientists would have to invent them to make the practice of science possible. In societies where these values did not exist, science has had to create them.

Science is not a mechanism but a human progress. To the layman who is dominated by the fallacy of the comic strips, that science would all be done best by machines, all this is puzzling. But human search and research is a learning by steps of which none is final, and the mistakes of one generation are rungs in the ladder, no less than their correction by the next. This is why the values of science turn out to be recognizably the human values: because scientists must be men, must be fallible, and yet as men must be willing and as a society must be organized to correct their errors. William Blake said that "to be an Error & to be Cast out is a part of God's design." It is certainly part of the design of science.

There never was a great scientist who did not make bold guesses, and there never was a bold man whose guesses were not sometimes wild. Newton was wrong, in the setting of his time, to think that light is made up of particles. Faraday was foolish when he looked in his setting for a link between electro-magnetism and gravitation. And such is the nature of science, their bad guesses may yet be brilliant by the work of our own day. We do not think any less of the profound concept of General Relativity in Einstein because the details of his formulation at this moment seem doubtful. For in science as in literature, the style of a great man is the stamp of his mind and makes even his mistakes a challenge which is part of the march of its subject. Science at last respects the scientist more than his theories, for by its nature, it must prize the search above the discovery and the thinking (and with it the thinker) above the thought. In the society of scientists each man, by the process of exploring for the truth, has earned a dignity more profound than his doctrine. A true society is sustained by the sense of human dignity.

I take this phrase from the life of the French naturalist Buffon who, like Galileo, was forced to recant his scientific findings. Yet he preserved always, says his biographer, something deeper than the fine manners of the court of Louis XV; he kept "le sentiment exquis. de la dignité humaine." His biographer says that Buffon learned this during his stay in England where it was impressed on him by the scientists he met. Since Buffon seems to have spent at most three months in England, this claim has been thought extravagant. But is it? Is history really so inhuman an arithmetic? Buffon in the short winter of 1738-9 met the grave men of the Royal Society, heirs to Newton, the last of a great generation. He found them neither a court nor a rabble, but a community of scientists seeking the truth together with dignity and humanity. It was, it is, a discovery to form a man's life.

The sense of human dignity that Buffon showed in his bearing is the cement of a society of equal men, for it expresses their knowledge that respect for others must be founded in self-respect. Theory and experiment alike become meaningless unless the scientist brings to them, and his fellows can assume in him, the respect of a lucid honesty with himself. The mathematician and philosopher W. K. Clifford said this forcibly at the end of his short life, nearly a hundred years ago.

> If I steal money from any person, there may be no harm done by the mere transfer of possession; he may not feel the loss, or it may even prevent him from using the money badly. But I cannot help doing this great wrong towards Man, that I make myself dishonest. What hurts society is not that it should lose its property, but that it should become a den of thieves; for then it must cease to be society. This is why we ought not to do evil that good may come; for at any rate this great evil has come, that we have done evil and are made wicked thereby.

This is the scientist's moral: that there is no distinction between ends and means. Clifford goes on to put this in terms of the scientist's practice.

> In like manner, if I let myself believe anything on insufficient evidence, there may be no great harm done by the mere belief; it may be true after all, or I may never have occasion to exhibit it in outward acts. But I cannot help doing this great wrong towards Man, that I make myself credulous. The danger to society is not merely that it should believe wrong things, though that is great enough; but that it should become credulous.

And the passion in Clifford's tone shows that to him the word credulous had the same emotional force as a 'den of thieves.'

The fulcrum of Clifford's ethic here, and mine, is the phrase "it may be true after all." Others may allow this to justify their conduct; the practice of science wholly rejects it. It does not admit that the word true can have this meaning. The test of truth is the fact, and no glib expediency nor reason of state can justify the smallest self-deception in that. Our work is of a piece, in the large and in detail, so that if we silence one scruple about our means, we infect ourselves and our ends together.

The scientist derives this ethic from his method, and every creative worker reaches it for himself. This is how Blake reached it from his practice as a poet and a painter.

> He who would do good to another must do it in
>   Minute Particulars:
> General Good is the plea of the scoundrel,
>   hypocrite & flatterer,
> For Art & Science cannot exist but in minutely
>   organized Particulars.

The Minute Particulars of art and the fine structure of science alike make the grain of conscience.

5.

Usually when scientists claim that their work has liberated men, they do so on more practical grounds.

In these four hundred years, they say, we have mastered sea and sky, we have drawn information from the electron and power from the nucleus, we have doubled the span of life and halved the working day, and we have enriched the leisure we have created with universal education and high-fidelity recordings and electric light and the lipstick. We have carried out the tasks which men set for us because they were most urgent. To a world population at least five times larger than in Kepler's day, there begins to be offered a life above the animal, a sense of personality, and a potential of human fulfilment, which make both the glory and the explosive problem of our age.

These claims are not confined to food and bodily comfort. Their larger force is that the physical benefits of science have opened a door and will give all men the chance to use mind and spirit. The technical man here neatly takes his model from evolution, in which the enlargement of the human brain followed the development of the hand.

I take a different view of science as a method; to me, it enters the human spirit more directly. Therefore I have studied quite another achievement: that of making a human society work. As a set of discoveries and devices, science has mastered nature; but it has been able to do so only because its values, which derive from its method, have formed those who practice it into a living, stable and incorruptible society. Here is a community where everyone has been free to enter,

86

to speak his mind, to be heard and contradicted; and it has outlasted the empires of Louis XIV and the Kaiser. Napoleon was angry when the Institute he had founded awarded his first scientific prize to Humphry Davy, for this was in 1807, when France was at war with England. Science survived then and since because it is less brittle than the rage of tyrants.

This is a stability which no dogmatic society can have. There is today almost no scientific theory which was held when, say, the Industrial Revolution began about 1760. Most often today's theories flatly contradict those of 1760; many contradict those of 1900. In cosmology, in quantum mechanics, in genetics, in the social sciences, who now holds the beliefs that seemed firm fifty years ago? Yet the society of scientists has survived these changes without a revolution and honors the men whose beliefs it no longer shares. No one has been shot or exiled or convicted of perjury; no one has recanted abjectly at a trial before his colleagues. The whole structure of science has been changed, and no one has been either disgraced or deposed. Through all the changes of science, the society of scientists is flexible and single-minded together and evolves and rights itself. In the language of science, it is a stable society.

The society of scientists is simple because it has a directing purpose: to explore the truth. Nevertheless, it has to solve the problem of every society, which is to find a compromise between man and men. It must encourage the single scientist to be independent, and the body of scientists to be tolerant. From these basic conditions, which form the prime values, there follows step by step the spectrum of values: dissent, freedom of thought and speech, justice, honor, human dignity and self-respect.

Our values since the Renaissance have evolved by just such steps. There are of course casuists who, when they are not busy belittling these values, derive them from the Middle Ages. But that servile and bloody world upheld neither independence nor tolerance, and it is from these, as I have shown, that the human values are rationally derived. Those who crusade against the rational and receive their values by mystic inspiration have no claim to these values of the mind. I cannot put this better than in the words of Albert Schweitzer in which he, a religious man, protests that mysticism in religion is not enough.

> Rationalism is more than a movement of thought which realized itself at the end of the eighteenth and the beginning of the nineteenth centuries. It is a necessary phenomenon in all normal spiritual life. All real progress in the world is in the last analysis produced by rationalism. The principle, which was then established, of basing our views of the universe on thought and thought alone is valid for all time.

So proud men have thought, in all walks of life, since Giordano Bruno was condemned to be burnt for his cosmology, about 1600. They have gone about their work simply enough. The scientists among them did not set out to be moralists or revolutionaries. William Harvey and Huygens, Euler and Avogadro, Darwin and Willard Gibbs and Marie Curie, Planck and Pavlov practiced their crafts modestly and steadfastly. Yet the values they seldom spoke of shone out of their work and entered their ages and slowly re-made the minds of men. Slavery ceased to be a matter of course. The princelings of Europe fled from the gaming table. The empires of the Bourbons and the Hapsburgs crumbled. Men asked for the rights of man and for government by consent. By the beginning of the nineteenth century, Napoleon did not find a scientist to elevate tyranny into a system; that was done by the philosopher Hegel. Hegel had written his university dissertation to prove philosophically that there could be no more than the seven planets he knew. It was unfortunate, and characteristic, that even as he wrote, on 1st January 1801, a working astronomer observed the eighth planet Ceres.

6.

I began this book with the question which has haunted me, as a scientist, since I heard it in the ruins of Nagasaki: "Is You Is Or Is You Ain't Ma Baby?" Has science fastened upon our society a monstrous gift of destruction which we can neither undo nor master, and which, like a clockwork automaton in a nightmare, is set to break our necks? Is science an automaton, and if so has it lamed our sense of values?

These questions are not answered by holding a Sunday symposium of moralists. They are not even answered by the painstaking neutralism of the textbooks on scientific method. We must indeed begin from a study of what scientists do, when they are neither posed for photographs on the steps of spaceships nor bumbling professorially in the cartoons. But we must get to the heart of what they do. We must lay bare the conditions which make it possible for them to work at all.

When we do so we find, leaf by leaf, the organic values which I have been unfolding. And we find that they are not at odds with the values by which alone mankind can survive. On the contrary, like the other creative activities which grew from the Renaissance, science has humanized our values. Men have asked for freedom, justice and respect precisely as the scientific spirit has spread among them. The dilemma of today is not that the human values cannot control a mechanical science. It is the other way about: the scientific spirit is more human than the machinery of governments. We have not let either the tolerance or the empiricism of science enter the parochial rules by which we still try to prescribe the behavior of nations. Our conduct as states clings to a code of self-interest which science, like humanity, has long left behind.

The body of technical science burdens and threatens us because we are trying to employ the body without the spirit; we are trying to buy the corpse of science. We are hag-ridden by the power of nature which we should command because we think its command needs less devotion and understanding than its discovery. And because we know how gunpowder works, we sigh for the days before atomic bombs. But massacre is not prevented by sticking to gunpowder; the Thirty Years' War is proof of that. Massacre is prevented by the scientist's ethic, and the poet's, and every creator's: that the end for which we work exists and is judged only by the means which we use to reach it. This is the human sum of the values of science. It is the basis of a society which scrupulously seeks knowledge to match and govern its power. But it is not the scientist who can govern society; his duty is to teach it the implications and the values in his work. Sir Thomas More said this in 1516, that the single-minded man must not govern but teach; and went to the scaffold for neglecting his own counsel.

7.

I have analysed in this book only the activity of science. Yet I do not distinguish it from other imaginative activities; they are as much parts one of another as are the Renaissance and the Scientific Revolution. The sense of wonder in nature, of freedom within her boundaries, and of unity with her in knowledge, is shared by the painter, the poet and the mountaineer. Their values, I have no doubt, express concepts as profound as those of science and could serve as well to make a society—as they did in Florence, and in Elizabethan London and among the famous doctors of Edinburgh. Every cast of mind has its creative activity which explores the likenesses appropriate to it and derives the values by which it must live.

The exploration of the artist is no less truthful and strenuous than that of the scientist. If science seems to carry conviction and recognition more immediately, this is because here the critics are also those who work at the matter. There is not, as in the arts, a gap between the functions (and therefore between the fashions) of those who comment and those who do. Nevertheless, the great artist works as devotedly to uncover the implications of his vision as does the great scientist. They grow, they haunt his thought, and their most inspired flash is the end of a lifetime of silent exploration. Turn to the three versions of *Faust* at which Goethe worked year in and year out. Or watch Shakespeare at work. Early in this book I quoted from *Romeo and Juliet* the image of death as a bee that stings other people, but that comes to Juliet to drink her sweetness—

Death that hath suckt the honey of thy breath.

More than ten years later Shakespeare came back to the image and unexpectedly made it concrete, a metaphor turned into a person in the drama. The drama is *Antony and Cleopatra*; the scene is the high tower;

92

and to it death comes in person, as an asp hidden among figs. The image of the asp carries, of course, many undertones; and most moving among these is Cleopatra's fancy that this death, which should sting, has come to her to suck the sweetness. Cleopatra is speaking, bitterly, tenderly, about the asp:

> Peace, peace:
> Dost thou not see my Baby at my breast,
> That suckes the Nurse asleepe.

The man who wrote these words still carried in his ear the echo from Juliet's tomb, and what he added to it was the span of his life's work.

Whether our work is art or science or the daily work of society, it is only the form in which we explore our experience which is different; the need to explore remains the same. This is why, at bottom, the society of scientists is more important than their discoveries. What science has to teach us here is not its techniques but its spirit: the irresistible need to explore. Perhaps the techniques of science may be practiced for a time without its spirit, in secret establishments, as the Egyptians practiced their priestcraft. But the inspiration of science for four hundred years has been opposite to this. It has created the values of our intellectual life and, with the arts, has taught them to our civilization. Science has nothing to be ashamed of even in the ruins of Nagasaki. The shame is theirs who appeal to other values than the human imaginative values which science has evolved. The shame is ours, if we do not make science part of our world, intellectually as much as physically, so that we may at last hold these halves of the world together by the same values. For this is the lesson of science, that the concept is more profound than its laws and the act of judging more critical than the judgment. In a book that I wrote about poetry I said:

> Poetry does not move us to be just or unjust, in itself. It moves us to thoughts in whose light justice and injustice are seen in fearful sharpness of outline.'

What is true of poetry is true of all creative thought. And what I said then of one value is true of all human values. The values by which we are to survive are not rules for just and unjust conduct, but are those deeper illuminations in whose light justice and injustice, good and evil, means and ends are seen in fearful sharpness of outline.